DOUNREAY

The illustrated story

DOUNREAY
The illustrated story

Stephen Cashmore

North of Scotland
NEWSPAPERS

Home of the John O'Groat Journal and Caithness Courier

Contents

Foreword

I well remember the immediate pre-Dounreay days when Donald Carmichael, well known in the county and already a good friend of many of us, came back to Caithness to prepare the way for the coming of the Atomic Energy Authority.

My late husband, Robin, then the Honourable Robin Sinclair, was at that time on both Thurso Town Council and a Caithness County Councillor and he, along with such stalwarts as Provost John Sinclair, Dr Sutherland, Hugh Macdonald and Sir Keith Murray, convener of the County Council, were quick to respond to Donald Carmichael's request for support for the Dounreay project.

The subsequent visits of Sir Donald Perrott and Sir Christopher Hinton to hold public meetings to inform local people about Dounreay remain fresh in my mind, even after the passing of more than 40 years.

Robin always insisted that the scientists who came to Dounreay in the early days, pioneers as they undoubtedly were, nevertheless had an integrity and honesty, and always gave him all the information he asked for to enable him to speak with authority during nuclear energy debates in the House of Lords.

Has the Dounreay project been beneficial to Caithness? I strongly believe so for, as well as providing first-class training and career opportunities for local people, Dounreay has also enhanced the social life of the county, building on existing foundations in the fields of drama, art and sport.

I have often wondered when a pictorial record of Dounreay would appear, and I am so glad that one has now been compiled and published by a Caithness company.

Margaret Thurso.

MARGARET THURSO

Acknowledgements

Many people contributed to the making of *Dounreay – The Illustrated Story*. The publishers acknowledge with gratitude the assistance and enthusiasm of the following, without whose co-operation this publication would not have been possible.

J. Les Brown, formerly of DMTR and Dounreay Technical Secretariat.
Laura Brown, designer of the DFR logo used throughout the book.
Sheona Campbell, North of Scotland Newspapers.
James Campbell, Graphics Department, Johnson Controls, Dounreay.
Margaret Carmichael, of Dorrery, by Halkirk.
Jimmy Crossan, formerly of DFR and Dounreay Training Department.
Julian Smith, Designsmith.
Ted Dowding, formerly UKAEA Architect for the Dounreay Fast Reactor project.
David Farquhar, formerly of Dounreay Health Physics.
Alistair Fraser, Contracts Department, UKAEA Dounreay.
Colin Gregory, Chief Technologist, UKAEA Dounreay.
John Gray, formerly of DFR and PFR, Dounreay.
The descendants of Henry Henderson, Bard of Reay.
Alan Hendry, North of Scotland Newspapers.
The Innes family of Buldoo.
Eric Jenkins, Graphics Department, AEAT, Harwell.
Geoff Leet, formerly of Dounreay Physics Group.
Anne Lyon, Graphics Department, Johnson Controls, Dounreay.
Kerry MacDougall, Graphics Department, Johnson Controls, Dounreay.

George Mackay, crofter, Buldoo.
John Macrae, former Dounreay photographer.
Derrick Milnes, formerly of Dounreay Communications Department.
Rab Murray, former Dounreay Transport driver.
Elizabeth Nicolson, Spittal, formerly of Lower Dounreay.
Mrs Jessie Oag, Wick, formerly of Lower Dounreay.
Morris Pottinger, Isauld, formerly of Lower Dounreay.
Clive Richards, North of Scotland Newspapers.
Catherine Ross, formerly of North of Scotland Newspapers.
Hugh Ross, Site Electrical Services, Johnson Controls, Dounreay.
Derek Shipley, formerly of DFR and PFR, Dounreay.
Willie Sloss, formerly of Fuel Technology Division, Dounreay.
Walter Smith, formerly of DMTR and PFR, Dounreay.
Peter Stephen, Graphics Department, Johnson Controls, Dounreay.
Jimmy Sutherland, formerly of BWD, Dounreay.
John Sutherland, formerly of D1200 Labs, Dounreay.
John Walford, formerly of Criticality Group, DFR, PFR and Safety Secretariat, Dounreay.
Tommy Wright formerly of Chemical Group, DFR and PFR, Dounreay. Ex-RNR (retired).

COPYRIGHT © 1998 NORTH OF SCOTLAND NEWSPAPERS

Unless otherwise stated, all the photographs in this book are the copyright © of the UKAEA.
Additional photographs are reproduced by kind permission of the following: Scotsman Publications Ltd.
Hulton Getty Picture Collection Ltd., and The Royal Commission on the Ancient and Historical Monuments of Scotland.

ISBN 1 871704 21 9

Produced and typeset by North of Scotland Newspapers, 42 Union Street, Wick, Caithness, Scotland.

Printed by Highland Printers, Henderson Road, Inverness, Scotland.
The typeface used throughout this book is Palatino. Printed on Magnomat Satin 135gsm.

A Catalogue Record of this book is available from the British Library.

Front cover: The sun setting on the sphere.   Half-title page: Construction workers leaving the site, March 1957.
Title page; main picture: PFR showing the Turbine Hall under construction.
Title page; inset: Prime symbol of the Nuclear Age, the DFR sphere nearing completion.
Front endpapers: The Dounreay site looking west from the top of the D1213 ventilation stack, July 1956 (Scotsman Publications Ltd.)
Back endpapers: The sphere under construction (Hulton Getty Picture Collection Ltd.)

Preface

From Caithness to the World

In the midsummer of 1955 a controversy arose regarding the pronunciation of an obscure Caithness place-name. Like most controversies conducted between learned people, it was a polite and dignified affair. A gentleman farmer supported his opinions by an appeal to the spoken language of the educated Caithnessians; his social equal, the son of a local minister, was apt to favour the pronunciation used by the farm servants and crofters who worked the land; and the third opinion – that of no less a national institution than the BBC – insisted on phonetic correctness.

After a lot of inconclusive correspondence between the principal parties in the dispute, appeal was made to K. H. Jackson, Professor of Gaelic at Edinburgh University. The Professor responded in very few words. The opinions of both the educated Caithnessian and the British Broadcasting Corporation could be safely ignored – the pronunciation used by the local people was, without a doubt, the correct one, and that was that.

Forty years and more have passed away and one may still find those willing to argue Professor Jackson's decision; one thing, however, is certain – no matter how it is pronounced, be it "Downreay", "Doonreay" or "Doonrä", the name is synonymous with the great nuclear research establishment built there in the 1950s.

7

Introduction

When, on March 1st, 1954, the Minister of Works, Sir David Eccles, informed the House of Commons of the Government's decision to build a nuclear reactor of the breeder type at Dounreay in Caithness, the likelihood was that few amongst his audience had anything but the vaguest notion of where the place actually was. One man who did know was Sir David Robertson, the Member for Caithness and Sutherland, who had been a redoubtable champion for the fast reactor project being located in his constituency. Sir David was a Conservative, but his personality eclipsed his political sympathies. He was one of those men, impatient of bureaucratic delays, scornful of talking-shop committees, and possessed of a mighty self-belief, whose only possible approach to a problem was to meet it head on. This attitude may be dangerously contagious, plunging whole sections of society into controversy. Sometimes, however, the consequences are beneficial far beyond any initial expectations. When Sir David was introduced to a man who was, in many respects, similar to himself, the ultimate outcome would prove advantageous to people not yet born in 1954. This man was Sir Christopher Hinton, chief of the Ministry of Supply's Atomic Energy Industrial Group, based at Risley in Cheshire.

If few MPs had heard of Dounreay, they were not alone; quite a number of Caithness residents knew little about it either. True, it had been a place to where certain well-to-do Thurso folk had leisurely driven the horse and trap on sunny summer weekends, but that had been before the construction of the Admiralty aerodrome in 1941 spoiled the view. The majority of Caithnessians had never been to Dounreay – indeed, why should they have? There was nothing there but a couple of good arable farms, and a few crofts.

One of the best aspects of an enlightened democracy is that important Government decisions very seldom come as a complete surprise. Some time before Sir David Eccles addressed the House, the canny Caithness folk had known that something big and exciting relating to Dounreay was about to be announced. Strangers with briefcases had been seen in the county even before the publicised visit of Sir Christopher Hinton in May 1953 when, accompanied by Sir David Robertson and everyone who was anyone in the Caithness administration, he had come to seek out a suitable site for the fast reactor. The Eccles announcement merely confirmed what everyone in Caithness had been longing so much to hear.

At a stroke it seemed as though, at long last, decades of slow economic wasting away were about to end. For long enough the Far North had been experiencing a lean season. Fishing and the flagstone industry, those one-time pillars of the local labour market, had seen their glory pass away; and in agriculture, creeping mechanisation was steadily reducing the demand for farm servants. With choice extinct, the only way to employment led south over the Ord. Caithness had long been exporting its finest product – people. Dounreay, it was hoped, was about to change all that. It did that and more, bringing back homesick exiles and introducing a new breed of Caithness resident – the "Atomics". It would be an interesting exercise for someone to predict just what the population and prosperity of Caithness might be today without the presence of the nuclear industry.

Months passed. In July 1954 the United Kingdom Atomic Energy Authority was set up as a body separate from the Ministry of Supply. Three months later the UKAEA took over administrative control of the Dounreay aerodrome from the Admiralty. Out at the site little appeared to have changed. A small party of engineers had visited Dounreay in June to make a few sample borings, but for most of the year the only visible sign that anything new was intended there was a small square hole cut in the turf near the foreshore. This marked the centre line of the fast reactor sphere. Apart from the handful of Admiralty maintenance staff painting the empty buildings, the Dounreay airfield remained the province of grazing sheep, its silence disturbed only by the piping cries of oystercatchers and the lonely sound of curlew call. Away from the site, however, constructive activity of a different kind was under way.

There were drawbacks associated with the siting of the fast reactor project at Dounreay. Caithness was an educated county, second only to Aberdeenshire in the proportion of scholars it sent on to become university graduates; but it was clearly lacking in the trained personnel required to staff a complex scientific establishment. The UKAEA estimated that half the initial labour force would have to be recruited from other areas, principally from the Authority's existing plants in the North of England. Would they be able to persuade these people to remove to Caithness? Once there, would they stay? Designing and building a nuclear reactor was a technical matter; importing the people to operate the thing was quite another. Integrating this collection of strangers into the existing community was something else again. Fortunately the UKAEA possessed social engineers every bit as able as their industrial counterparts.

In the Caithness County Council and the Thurso Town Council the UKAEA found willing collaborators. A strong sense of common purpose prevailed. A prime requirement was housing for the hundreds of permanent staff expected to arrive in Thurso during the next few years. This was a very tall order for a small local authority. By a stroke of good fortune, Thurso Town Council had retained its powers as an independent planning authority, requiring no sanction from Edinburgh. Nevertheless, the obstacles facing it were formidable, not least raising the wherewithal to finance the construction of over 1000 new homes. However, assistance was forthcoming from both the UKAEA and the Scottish Special Housing Association; by the beginning of 1955 the conversion of the Ormlie Hotel into a hostel for Authority staff had commenced, and work had started on building the first row of houses in Thorfinn Terrace.

That the news of Dounreay's forthcoming role in the development of the nuclear power industry was welcome throughout the Far North cannot be denied. But doubts did exist, and quite rightly so, for an educated population is never a docile one. Fears were expressed about the dangers of radiation, the possibility of the reactor blowing up – remember, it was scarcely 10 years since the destruction of Hiroshima had ushered in the Nuclear Age. Partly to allay these fears, but more so to inform the Caithness public of just what the UKAEA intended to do at Dounreay, Sir Christopher Hinton arrived in Caithness on Monday, January 3rd, 1955. The next morning he held an informal meeting with the dozen crofters soon to become the UKAEA's neighbours. The meeting took place in the airfield control tower, a cold place green with mildew. On one table stood a model of the atomic site, on another a tray of New Year refreshments. In the words of the venerable Bard o' Reay, 81-year-old Henry Henderson, who stayed at Buldoo, Christopher Hinton "just sat on a table swinging his legs – and talked".

That evening Sir Christopher talked again, this time to a crowd of over 600 people shoe-horned into Thurso Town Hall. His lecture lasted 90 minutes. He spoke frankly and in a straightforward manner comprehensible to his audience. He was never patronising or evasive, nor did he attempt to blind his listeners with scientific claptrap. Long before the term became common currency in public relations, Sir Christopher Hinton clearly understood what "stakeholders" meant.

Came the end of February, 1955, with the heavy snowfalls of January 12th and February 17th here and away, and the UKAEA's purchase of the farms of Isauld and Lower Dounreay completed, the civil engineering contractors began to move in in force. By March 29th Whatlings of Glasgow had 250 men working at Dounreay, digging out the foundations for the fast reactor.

The construction of Dounreay was an epic in its own right. The building of two reactors – a Materials Testing Reactor had been added to the original concept – fuel fabrication plants, reprocessing facilities, laboratories, waste stores, workshops, offices, etc., occupied up to 3000 men for over three years. Half of those engaged were locals. One man who worked in the joinery workshop had no doubt that it was the high-time of his life. Constant friendly banter and at least one rough-and-tumble fight a week, not to mention the wages. Some declared their working day to be 25 hours long – 24 hours' work plus an hour out for lunch.

The popular press had a field day. The camp, a collection of refurbished ex-Admiralty huts just to the south of the Dounreay site, in which the majority of the contractors were housed, was represented as a modern-day Wild West boom-town. The combination of high wages and devil-may-care roughnecks was deemed a sure recipe for lawlessness. And (additional horror) work went on seven days a week, including Sunday. No doubt unruly behaviour did exist, but the truth was generally more mundane. The on-schedule construction of such a large site remote from all sources of supply, having more manpower than mechanical aid, within so brief a timespan, hardly suggests an ill-disciplined workforce.

On Saturday, May 11th, 1957, Far North folk flocked in their thousands to the site's first Open Day. Simultaneously, exhibitions explaining the Dounreay Fast Reactor were staged in Thurso Town Hall, Inverness and at the Art Gallery in Aberdeen. The public seemed well-pleased, especially as the UKAEA had recently commenced building a test reactor at Dounreay for the Navy's nuclear submarine programme. This was expected to provide another 250 jobs, half of which it was reasonable to suppose would be filled by local people.

And now came the second stage in the great Dounreay project – the gathering of information that would determine the suitability of fast breeder reactors as power sources for electricity generation. The reactors had been built, nearly fifteen hundred workers were now on the UKAEA payroll at Dounreay, some of them recently flitted from the south into the new houses fast rising on the west side of Thurso, others settled into the semi-institutionalised life at Ormlie Lodge Hostel. The hardware was in place; the brains were assembled; £28 million had been spent. Would it all come together? That was the critical question.

The UKAEA took formal possession of the Dounreay Fast Reactor from its builders, Motherwell Bridge, on May 26th, 1957, following four days of pressure and vacuum tests on its distinctive containment sphere. The target was to achieve the first controlled nuclear chain reaction, or criticality, in the Dounreay Fast Reactor sometime in April 1958. At 0245hrs on May 24th, 1958, sensitive low power range instruments indicated that criticality was under way in a reactor at Dounreay. But it was not the fast reactor that went critical on that date – it was its little brother, the recently commissioned DMTR.

The Dounreay Materials Testing Reactor was the twin of PLUTO, one of two MTRs already in operation at the UKAEA's Harwell establishment. The highly-enriched uranium fuel for these reactors was fabricated at Dounreay in the MTR Fuel Fabrication Plant (D1202) and the first batch of spent fuel from Harwell had just gone through the MTR Reprocessing Plant (D1204).

At the end of 1958 commissioning of the fast reactor got under way. It was a time of rising excitement and high expectations. The staff put in long, long hours, everyone being dedicated to ensuring the success of this ground-breaking experiment. At last, at 1052hrs on Saturday, November 14th, 1959, the Control Room instruments showed clearly that the Dounreay Fast Reactor had ceased to be a theory – it was now a fact. The staff, some of whom had been on duty throughout the night, were quietly satisfied, relieved at the smooth accomplishment of this major step. Within an hour work had started on the reactor's Zero Energy Programme.

Now began those tasks for which the fast reactor had been intended: investigations into every aspect of its physical behaviour, and the irradiation of the various types of fuel designed to be used in any future family of big, electricity-generating reactors of the breeder type. The DFR fuel cycle was a self-contained entity on the Dounreay site. New fuel was fabricated in D1201, it was loaded into DFR, irradiated, removed to a cooling pond before being sent to the Fast Reactor Fuel Reprocessing Plant (D1206). From D1206 the recovered fissile material went to D1203, Uranium Recovery Facility, where it was turned into billets, ready for dispatch to D1201, where the whole cycle started over again. The commercial by-product of all this was the electricity generated by DFR, the first 2 megawatts of which were fed into the National Grid on October 2nd, 1962. It was the first commercially exported fast reactor-generated electricity in the world. Less than a year later, on July 5th, 1963, DFR's maximum electrical output of 14.5 megawatts was achieved.

But this was not all. The DMTR was busy irradiating specimens of all kinds of materials intended for potential use in future fast reactors, at a radiation intensity roughly 10 times greater than was possible in its larger brother. These specimens, along with samples of DFR irradiations, were being dismembered in specially shielded post-irradiation examination facilities such as D1217. Reprocessing campaigns went on, supported by chemical and metallurgical laboratories in the D1200 complex; and radioactive waste of all kinds, both liquid and solid, was being handled, segregated, stored, discharged and disposed of in ways that were often highly innovative. Over everything there ruled a first-class administration, and a health and safety organisation which ensured that every operation was carried out in strict conformity with the UKAEA's own high standards, as well as with relevant legislation, such as the Factories Act.

Ancillary to all this was the ongoing large-scale research into the technology of sodium and sodium/potassium (NaK), the liquid metals used both to cool the fast reactor core and to transfer the core's heat to the steam-generating units. This was frontier technology; so, too, was the work going on in the mechanical and electrical laboratories, where instrumentation was being developed to detect overheating in fuel pins by listening for minute sound fluctuations, and small test rigs were investigating the corrosive effects of sodium in simulated reactor core conditions. Meanwhile, the highly skilled staff necessary for all this work were being trained in all the various disciplines – scientific, engineering, clerical, administrative – required by this vast project. The first engineering apprentices began training as early as September 1955. In January 1960, a purpose-built on-site Apprentice Training School opened its doors. Two years later, 70 apprentices moved into the new Naver House hostel.

Outwith the main site, work went on apace building houses for the new arrivals in Thurso – the so-called "Atomics". New schools were built or planned, a technical college sprang up on the western fringe of Thurso to augment the Dounreay on-site training facilities. Recreational needs were not forgotten; in April 1958, the UKAEA acquired a large house called "Viewfirth" and began transforming it into a cosy home for the Dounreay Sports and Social Club. The whole of Caithness basked in the warmth of this new economic and cultural prosperity which the fast reactor project had brought to the county. There were, inevitably, a few dissenting voices. One lady complained that shopping was not the pleasure it once had been. The Thurso shops were crowded with newcomers; queues sometimes formed, and shopkeepers no longer had unlimited leisure to blether with customers. Not surprisingly, no-one from the Thurso commercial fraternity could be found to endorse these complaints.

All these various strands of the Dounreay project were like streams feeding into a mighty river whose source was the fast reactor. As it flowed on through a virgin scientific landscape, this river swelled with an astonishing variety of new-proven theories, improved techniques, unexpected discoveries, fresh-trodden scientific byways. People came and went, many well-pleased with what they found, others muttering sullenly about "that God-forsaken place". And this great river of scientific and social achievement was flowing on towards a single goal – the Prototype Fast Reactor.

From the outset it was apparent that the DFR was only one stage en route to the 1000-megawatt commercial fast breeder reactors which, it was assumed, would be coming on line during the 1980s. DFR had its predecessors, ZEPHYR and ZEUS, two small-scale affairs, built at Harwell to prove the fundamental physics of fast reactors. This basic scientific information DFR had refined into a working technology. If DFR was applied science, PFR would be applied technology. The next logical development was to demonstrate that this technology could be put to use on a scale large enough to show that fast breeders could compete with other reactor types in the field of commercial electricity generation. That Dounreay would be the site of the proposed Prototype Fast Reactor appeared to be a foregone conclusion to most people.

In the decade prior to 1964 the population of Thurso had almost trebled; over 9000 now lived there.

Between them the UKAEA and the local authorities had built 1500 new houses, the rates from which put £37,000 per annum into the civic purse. A quarter of the population were registered car owners – a very high proportion for those days. Thurso boasted a supermarket and a bookshop; a fruiterer sold avocado pears. At its Dounreay site the UKAEA employed 2400 staff, 1300 of these being local people. In many ways the term "boom-town" appeared entirely justified. Then it seemed as though it was all about to come to a sudden premature end.

In March of 1964, the Transport Minister, Ernest Marples, was considering a proposal to close the railway line between Inverness and the Far North. This was alarming news. Worse still, though, was a credible rumour that the PFR was not, after all, to be built at Dounreay; the UKAEA's sites at Winfrith, in Dorset, and Chapelcross, Dumfriesshire, were reckoned more likely candidates. Morale slumped. The whole county shuddered at the spectre of economic ruin, population drain, all the evils of the immediate pre-Dounreay era. The single-employer dependency of the Caithness economy suddenly zoomed into sharp focus. A campaign was straight away set in motion to apply the necessary political pressure to ensure that the PFR came to Dounreay. The County Clerk wrote a very persuasive letter to the Secretary of State for Scotland, outlining Dounreay's case. On February 9th, 1966, the House of Commons was informed of the Government's approval of the UKAEA's plans to build the Prototype Fast Reactor – at Dounreay. Some believe, perhaps with good reason, that this decision was prompted by the needs of a small-majority government to hold onto power. No matter – the whole North of Scotland breathed and slept easier. And trains continued to arrive at Wick and Thurso stations.

The PFR opening ceremony took place on site on midsummer's day, 1966. Construction began immediately after. Although the two reactors shared the basic common features of a small core cooled by liquid metal, their many differences bear testimony to the success of DFR in continually advancing the original fast reactor design. Although the PFR core was barely three times the size of its predecessor's, it generated ten times more heat – 600 megawatts as opposed to 60; and this heat was convertible into 250 megawatts of electricity, a considerable improvement on DFR's nominal maximum of 15 megawatts, and a clear gain in thermal efficiency. There were other differences. The PFR core was situated within a steel and concrete-lined hole cut out of the Caithness rock. The containment building, a plain, concrete-clad rectangular structure, lacked the visual charisma of the DFR dome. Nevertheless, despite its uninspiring exterior, PFR was more than a little impressive, especially inside the Reactor Hall where, from 1978, public tour parties gazed with admiration on the array of huge steel flasks lined up along the wall of the irradiated fuel cave. Unlike DFR, its successor was designed to burn an oxide fuel, the fabrication of which would be carried out at BNFL's Windscale works, instead of at Dounreay. And there was the fundamental difference that, while DFR was an experimental tool, the new fast reactor was designed to function more as a power station. Built with the greater aid of machinery, with few of the labour force imported from the south, the construction history of PFR had little of the romance associated with the pick, shovel, brawn and sweat methods of the original site builders.

A year after work started on PFR, Caithness was disturbed by another rumour. A minute leak from the DFR primary cooling system caused the reactor to be shut down in July 1967. This leak being within the concrete vault surrounding the reactor, into which no access existed, raised fears that DFR would never restart. Some members of the Dounreay staff considered taking out insurance to protect themselves against redundancy. In the event, their fears were ill-founded. After a well conceived and executed campaign of engineering design and planning, the DFR leak was located and repaired, and the reactor restarted in June 1968.

A year after DFR resumed operation, the DMTR closed down for the last time. It had been a largely trouble-free performer for over ten years but, as much of its intended work on fast reactor fuel research had now been completed, it was deemed surplus to requirements. Economic necessity probably had no small part in the decision to close DMTR; since the early '60s a chill wind had been blowing through the corridors of nuclear power. Some people, among them prominent politicians, were beginning to question the apparent poor returns on the public's considerable financial outlay on nuclear technology, including the fast breeder reactor programme. No matter, work went ahead on the PFR. It was completed in 1973, fuel was loaded early next year, and low-power operations commenced in March 1974.

Elsewhere on the Dounreay site, other work was in progress. On April 6th, 1970, for the first time in two decades, a plane took off from the Dounreay airfield. This was the start of the charter service which was to carry hundreds of staff between Dounreay and UKAEA's Northern Division HQ at Risley. Many of these passengers were involved in the PFR project; others were busy on the next major Dounreay milestone – the refurbishing of chemical separation plants and laboratories in preparation for the reprocessing of fuel from the PFR.

In 1972 the normal routine of D1206, the DFR reprocessing facility, was turned upside down by the arrival of contractors armed with thermal lances. These men set to work with a will, stripping the concrete from the walls of the Blanket Cave, an unused facility originally intended for dismantling DFR breeder elements. For the next seven years, almost the entire Fuel Cycle Area was affected by the drastic modifications necessary to convert its basic function of dealing with the old uranium-based DFR fuels to one capable of handling the plutonium/uranium oxide mixtures burned in the PFR. While all this work was in progress, the plants continued reprocessing fuel from the DFR, as well as the highly-enriched uranium fuel arising from Dounreay's ongoing supply and reprocessing contracts with various research reactors worldwide.

11

By the time D1206 was ready to receive its first spent fuel from PFR, the first Dounreay Fast Reactor had, on March 28th, 1977, closed down for good; its final batch of fuel had been reprocessed; and the PFR had been supplying electricity to the National Grid since the beginning of 1975. By the summer of 1980, there was a pressing need to start reprocessing PFR fuel. Suddenly, D1206 became the most important building in the whole UKAEA. It responded accordingly.

The first PFR fuel reprocessing campaign got under way on September 16th, 1980. Certain improvements in the plant were suggested by the results of this initial campaign, but this was only to be expected at Dounreay, where scarcely a week went by without some new innovation coming to light – many of these new ideas originating with the site's excellent suggestions scheme.

During the 1980s, as a philosophy of public spending restraint became politically fashionable, Dounreay gradually began to lose its atmosphere of scientific research unfettered by the constraints of time and finance. On the positive side, in 1982 the first recycled plutonium from PFR was returned to the reactor, so closing the final link in the fuel cycle. But the PFR itself was experiencing problems – not with the reactor, which had proved to be a great success, but with the steam-generating units in the non-nuclear side of the plant. But as PFR was, to all intents and purposes, still part of a great experiment, many felt that problem-solving was what it was all about. It certainly seemed that way, especially as in 1983, the Secretary of State for Energy announced that Britain had started formal negotiations with its European partners for the pooling of information and resources towards the construction of a large European Fast Reactor, or EFR. A year later, Dounreay staff were a little surprised to hear that, in the event of the EFR project going ahead, Britain would not be the location of the reactor; the European Demonstration Reprocessing Plant, however, would come to Dounreay, subject to the outcome of a public inquiry.

The 95-day EDRP inquiry started in Thurso Town Hall on April 7th, 1986. It played to largely empty houses, a far cry from the historic Hinton lecture of 31 years before. This lack of public interest may have been indifference; it was more likely a measure of just how accepted Dounreay had become in Caithness. A week before the EDRP inquiry began hearing evidence, the UKAEA became a trading fund. This was the first step to what many regarded as an impossibility – the privatisation of parts of the Authority. Others saw the trading fund as the thin end of the wedge.

Meanwhile, its steam-generation problems apparently behind it, the PFR went on its way, reaching full electrical output in March 1985, and achieving record fuel burn-up figures during the first half of 1988. Then came the bombshell. On Thursday, July 21st, 1988, the Secretary of State for Energy, Cecil Parkinson, informed Parliament of the Government's decision to cease funding the PFR project beyond March 1994. The reprocessing plant would continue to receive public money until 1997, when it too would close, unless alternative sources of income could be found. Many at Dounreay that afternoon felt as though the Last Day was at hand. Positive talk of EFR or EDRP was heard no more.

Considerable efforts were made to reverse the Government's fast reactor policy. Adversity united workers, management, politicians and businesses throughout the Highlands. Adversity also threw up numerous prophets of doom who foresaw the years of the lean kine fast approaching Caithness. The announcement that the Government's radioactive waste executive, NIREX, intended to carry out test borings to ascertain the suitability of Dounreay as the location of its planned repository was received with a mixture of indifference and cynical resentment. Some of the wider Caithness community took a vote on the issue, the outcome being a "No to Nirex".

At midnight on March 31st, 1994, the PFR shut down for the last time. It ended its productive life in a blaze of glory with a record-breaking power-generation run, which followed hard on the heels of a significant engineering achievement – the removal, inspection and replacement of all three primary sodium pump filters. Next month the UKAEA was split into two parts, Government Division and AEA Technology. A year later and Dounreay's Facilities Services Division, which carried out much of the non-nuclear work at the site, was sold to Procord. It seemed as though an era had come to an end.

The worst predictions of the 1988 doom merchants have failed to materialise. While there is no denying that the Dounreay labour force is not what it was, no-one on the site was made compulsorily redundant. Indeed, many of those who have left the Authority's service since 1988 have taken generous financial compensation with them. The figure predicted by the Parkinson announcement – 500 Dounreay employees after 1997 – has turned out to be inaccurate, over three times that number being at work on site at that date. Furthermore, AEAT became a plc in 1996, defying the opinions of many who thought that no investor would be interested in risking money on a business that had its origins in the nuclear industry.

The Dounreay story is far from over. The PFR project did not come to an abrupt end at midnight on March 31st, 1994. There remained three complex decommissioning stages. The first stage involves the removal of the fuel from the reactor, achieved in 1995 ahead of schedule, and the removal, treatment and disposal of the 1500 tonnes of liquid metal coolant, some of it lightly contaminated, which is currently under way. The second stage, which involves the removal of all loose contamination from the plant, and the third stage, during which the reactor structure is removed, lie well into the future. All over the site the emphasis has changed from reactor operation to a regime of decommissioning redundant nuclear facilities, repackaging radioactive waste and improving existing techniques for achieving these aims, as well as developing new methods to deal with the significant tasks which lie ahead. The proposed removal of material from the disused radioactive waste shaft is but one of the challenges awaiting the ingenuity of nuclear engineers. The removal of the DFR breeder elements is another. And while waste management may lack the glamour of operating large reactors, it is every bit as important a component in the overall nuclear equation.

Safety has always been of paramount importance at Dounreay. In 1990 Dounreay became a nuclear licensed site subject to the terms of the Nuclear Installations Act and answerable to the Nuclear Installations Inspectorate (NII). The UKAEA has continued to operate with a proper regard for matching and bettering current safety standards, an ethos which extends to the growing body of contractors employed on the site.

There remain the pros and cons to consider. That the UKAEA's decision to site its great fast reactor project at Dounreay brought wealth, economic stability and cultural diversity to Caithness, no-one can reasonably dispute. That it arrested the decline of the county's population – especially amongst the young – is likewise a proven fact. Dounreay brought jobs to Caithness; but it also brought careers. Many who started their working lives in the capable hands of Mr William Sutherland, the Engineering Instructor at the original Apprentice Training School, are now occupying senior positions in companies throughout the world. Some stayed at home, happy to live, work and spend their money in the county of their birth. Without Dounreay, where would these people be now?

The ultimate aim of the fast reactor programme – a commercially viable power station and supporting fuel cycle – has not materialised, and therefore, some maintain, the whole thing has been a colossal waste of money. Let this accusation be answered in plain terms. The Government asked the UKAEA to build an experimental fast reactor. It did so, and the thing worked. Ten years later, a more powerful reactor was deemed necessary. This, too, the UKAEA designed, built and proved operational. More than enough information has been gathered to build a commercial fast reactor and its associated fuel cycle when the need arises. In the meantime, the nature of the challenge has changed to demonstrating that waste can be managed safely and decommissioning achieved economically. In terms of the future acceptance of nuclear power, these topics are as important now as demonstrating the fundamental physics, engineering and chemistry was in the '50s and '60s.

In recent years a considerable amount of media coverage has been given to past operations at Dounreay which, with the benefits of hindsight, the experience and knowledge gained over 40 years of operation, and the increasingly strict safety and environmental regulations, would not be deemed acceptable today. Without such benefits, staff operated and made decisions in good faith, based upon the knowledge available and within the regulations and authorisations current at the time. Nevertheless there are issues which need to be addressed, and rightly so. The present management has accepted the need to deal with the legacies of the past, and indeed various remediation programmes are already under way. Meanwhile, the media debate between the conflicting interests of critics and workers continues.

On a March afternoon in 1994, a few days before the PFR completed its final power-generation run, a young Authority engineer arrived in the Control Room with his father, a Caithness farmer who had never visited Dounreay, never had any interest in the place, except that his son earned his living there. The Control Room Desk Operator, a man of comparable age with the farmer, and himself a Caithnessian, showed his visitor round, pointing out to him all the different charts, lights, gauges and other indicators of the plant's current state, which showed that the PFR was exporting 240 megawatts of electricity to the National Grid, generating an income for Dounreay of some £90,000 per day.

The farmer asked the Control Room man how long he had been on site. "Just over 35 years," came the reply. "Dounreay's been good for the county, wouldn't you say?"

"Aye, I suppose it has," the farmer agreed. It was his final word on the subject. And mine.

ACRONYMS USED IN THIS BOOK

DFR Dounreay Fast Reactor

DMTR Dounreay Materials Testing Reactor

PFR Prototype Fast Reactor

NaK Sodium/Potassium Alloy, the liquid metal used to cool the DFR core.

CHAPTER ONE

The Pre-Atomic Age

With good reason has it been said that all seasons can be experienced in a single Caithness day; and equally true is it that no two days together in the Far North are ever quite the same. One morning may break soft and balmy, a featherweight breeze scarcely rippling the fringes of the great northern ocean; next day a roaring nor'-wester is driving those same waters helter-skelter onto the fractured flagstone foreshore, where they burst in wild white arabesques.

Then there are those events by which Nature marks the passing seasons. In May when the terns arrive, hard on the heels of a dense sea haar, to begin nesting just beyond the high tide line; and when skeins of honking greylag geese mark time in the twilight October sky, seeking familiar landmarks to point them on their migratory way. The UKAEA constable on his shoreline patrol sees these things just as surely as the first dwellers in this beautiful, lonely land saw them. They are timeless, beyond history in its narrow chronological sense.

> "And long may the lamps in your window set
> Be as stars to light my footsteps, when
> In the gloaming hour I shall wander yet
> In the Dounreay fields, as in boyhood, then
> Down to the shore and along the braes
> Where so oft I wandered in early days."

From a poem by Henry Henderson, Bard of Reay. 1873-1957.

Early energy innovations at Dounreay: Hamish Innes of Buldoo and the electricity-generating windmill he built in 1930.
By kind permission of the Innes family of Buldoo.

Dounreay Castle: Probably built in the late 16th century by Donald, Lord Reay, it was inhabited for almost 300 years.

Jack Davidson and his uncle, Jack, of Buckies, on the beach at Dounreay c.1932. Jack owned Lower Dounreay from 1930 until his death on active service in 1943. A Major with the 5th Seaforth Highlanders, Jack Davidson won the DSO fighting in North Africa.
By kind permission of Elizabeth Nicolson.

Jack Davidson's wife, Isobel, with their daughter Elizabeth on the steps of Lower Dounreay farmhouse, c. 1941.

Dounreay Castle and farm buildings from the beach showing the drainage pipe installed by Jack Davidson.

An aerial view of the Admiralty's airfield at Dounreay in 1946. The mile-long main runway was the longest north of Inverness.

By kind permission of the RCAHMS.

Farm buildings at Lower Dounreay immediately prior to the coming of the UKAEA.

The Dounreay Airfield control tower and administration buildings.

"I was here first." The Spitfire pilot who landed at Dounreay in 1942 with a fishing rod for the airfield's CO shows his logbook to George Plummer during a visit to the Dounreay Exhibition in 1979.

In 1946 the Admiralty camp at Dounreay was home to a group of displaced Polish servicemen, two of whom are seen here with a camp pet.
By kind permission of the Innes family of Buldoo.

Near neighbours: George, Murdo and Anne MacBeath of Lybster, Forss, seen here in the early 1950s with Hamish Innes's motor car.
By kind permission of Mrs Ina MacBeath, of Lybster, Forss.

Local folk: Buldoo, 1950. Henry Henderson, the celebrated "Bard of Reay", left, and George Mackay, who wrote as "Jenny Horne", right, with Mrs George Mackay and a visitor.
By kind permission of the descendants of Henry Henderson.

Maggie Henderson, wife of the Bard, outside Downreay Post Office, July 1933.
By kind permission of the descendants of Henry Henderson.

As things were: A turf-roofed house at Achreamie, by Dounreay, c.1945.
By kind permission of the descendants of Henry Henderson.

Lower Dounreay farm from the air in 1954, shortly after its purchase by Morris Pottinger.

The pre-Atomic town: Thurso town centre, 1954.

Thurso employment prospects, 1954: George Ross's pre-cast works.

CHAPTER TWO

"A Big Test Reactor . . . at Dounreay in Caithness"

'I must say a word about the plant at Dounreay. For safety's sake it will be housed in a large, spherical steel shell. But even when it is in that 'Dome of Discovery' . . . there is a very remote possibility of a slight leakage of radioactivity should there be a failure in certain parts of the plant. The local authorities have been consulted and with their help arrangements will be made as to what should be done in this most unlikely event. And I must emphasise that it is a *most* unlikely event."

Extract from Sir David Eccles's announcement of March 1st, 1954, when he informed the House of Commons of the Government's intention to build an experimental fast breeder reactor at Dounreay, and of the risk associated with the project. A local poet hinted at the Caithness public's apprehension of this risk, but he placed it in a wider historical context:

"Kaithness hes hed a wild career
O' bloodshed an' commotion;
She michtna hev so muckle more
If Dounreay tak's 'e notion!"

By "Castlegreen" (Donald Grant)

Left – Sir Christopher Hinton, chief of the Atomic Energy Authority's Industrial Group, and the man responsible for the Dounreay Fast Reactor project.

Bottom – The dream in miniature: The model of the site which was shown to the Dounreay residents who met Christopher Hinton in the airfield control tower on January 4th, 1955.

Right – Ormlie Lodge in January, 1955, shortly after the AEA bought it for conversion into a staff hostel.
By kind permission of Ted Dowding.

Middle right – January 13th, 1955: AEA employees' cars snowbound on Scrabster Hill after the worst blizzard in living memory.
By kind permission of Ted Dowding.

Bottom right – February 1955: Snow again. Members of the AEA's Risley planning team at Scrabster inspecting a boat which offered to take them through the Pentland Firth to Wick, the roads and railway being blocked with snow. Sensibly, perhaps, the Risley men refused this alternative transport.
By kind permission of Ted Dowding.

Bottom left – Making the best of it: January 15th, 1955. Site architect Ted Dowding with Mrs Margaret Carmichael and her daughter Jane, outside Mackay's Hotel, Scrabster. They are awaiting the return from Dounreay, by lifeboat, of Margaret's husband, Donald Carmichael.
By kind permission of Ted Dowding.

Where it all began: The Nissen hut which housed the first AEA personnel. Later, as building DN065, it was home to the Photographic Section from 1958 to 1984.

A sign of the times: The UKAEA posts notice that Lower Dounreay is under new ownership.

Whatlings get down to business: Preparing the track for the 30-ton crane, May 1955.

The May gobs: The fledgling site shivers after a snowstorm, May 13th, 1955.

Putting in the drain from the site to the beach.

Future visitors by appointment only: Erecting the site security fence.

Arrival of the steelmen: Motherwell Bridge take delivery of the manipulator which will be used to form and weld together pairs of steel plates for the fast reactor sphere.

Firm foundations: Preparing the 10-foot deep concrete raft which will support the fast reactor.

CHAPTER THREE

Theories in Stone and Concrete

From all over they came, an army of iron-fighters, concrete cowboys, pick-and-shovel earth-shifters, veterans of a hundred construction campaigns, bona fide representatives of the true race of "here today and gone tomorrow" Travelling Men, come to turn seaside fields into the greatest industrial complex ever seen in the Far North.

For three years, day-in, day-out, in all weathers, the work went on apace. Nothing stopped it, not even the Sabbath Day. In driving sleet, biting wind, dismal rain, and on days when a blustering gale blew from all directions at once, the construction gangs toiled on the Dounreay site. Long hours, bulging pay pokes. For the genuine Travelling Man a philosophy of "easy come, easy go" has ever been second nature, a profitable character defect for some sections of the local community. Here's what "Castlegreen" had to say on the subject:

"There's some fowk smilan' at 'e thocht o' 'at invadan' throng;
'E pubs 'll aal be busy an' 'e nicht-clubs goan' strong;
An' 'e merchants 'll be winkan'
Fan they're thinkan' o' 'e chinkan'
O' aal 'at soothern siller 'at'll come thur wey 'fore long."

The Dounreay Fast Reactor foundations showing the outer wall under construction.

August 1955: Completing the first row of plates for the base of the fast reactor sphere.

August 1955: The foundations for the Materials Testing Reactor (DMTR).

DMTR Heavy Water Plant Room walls taking shape.

DFR: Welding a cable block to the inner wall of a sphere plate.

DFR: Manoeuvring a sphere plate into position.

September 1955: The completed lower half of the DFR sphere.

On top of the world: A spiderman poses in the airlock space of the DFR sphere.

Typical Whatlings construction plant: An excavator discharges spoil into a dumper truck.

Pouring concrete for the founds of the Post-Irradiation Examination Building, D1217.

Light in the darkness: Silhouetted against the northern night sky, the half-built DFR sphere and its cranes form a dramatic image for a visiting *Picture Post* cameraman.
By kind permission of the Hulton Getty Picture Collection Ltd.

The largest hole on site: The D1208 Highly Active Liquor Storage Facility.

Whatlings joiners' shop: The figure centre right is Bill Durrand, later to become a Shift Foreman in the D1206 reprocessing plant.

Emerging from the depths of the 1-in-3 entrance adit to the Low Active Liquid Effluent Tunnel.

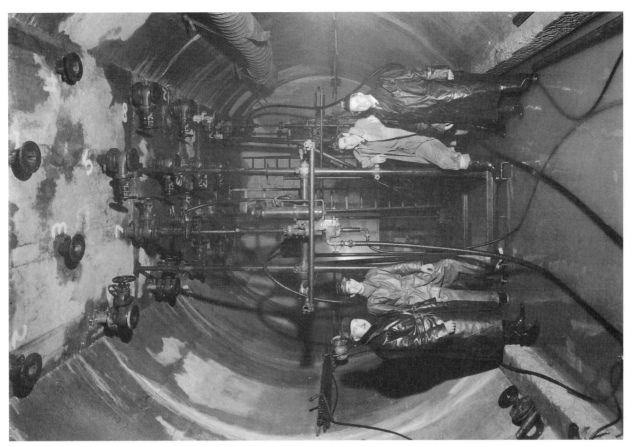

The end of the line: The effluent tunnel dispersal chamber.

Whatlings human moles riding on one of the trucks used to bring up freshly-excavated spoil from the effluent tunnel.

Construction went on around the clock: Night work in the DFR seawater inlet channel.

Inside a steel basilica: Looking up to the access hole in the top of the DFR sphere.

Summer 1956: Work in progress on the top half of the DFR sphere.

Staff relaxing in Whatlings Staff Club at the accommodation camp.
By kind permission of Alistair Fraser.

UKAEA staff sampling the liquid delights of Ormlie Lodge Bar, April 1957.

Housing for the "Atomics": Alexander Hall's men hard at work on the Pennyland scheme.

Rotterdam Street, Thurso, 1957.

DFR internal work: The base of the reactor's biological shield.

D1211 Liquid Effluent Pits foundations, September 1956.

Erecting the steel framework for Building D1204, the MTR fuel reprocessing plant.

Constructing the foundations of the site's Number 2 electricity sub-station.

Learning the trade: Craft apprentices from the 1956 intake gather round instructor William Sutherland as he demonstrates the finer points of lathe operation.
By kind permission of Hugh Ross.

Judging the work of the first craft apprentices, July 1956: The original apprentice training school was located at the old Admiralty camp.

Looking west over the site from the top of the Chemical Group's 180-foot high ventilation stack, D1213.

Above – Lowering the steel tank into the DMTR reactor shield block.

Left – Essential cleanliness: Removing all traces of loose impurities from the DMTR graphite shield.

Blasting out the DFR seawater pumphouse channel: David Thornton, aged 29, a London-born diver, prepares to place an underwater explosive charge.

April 1957: The DFR reactor vessel arrives in Caithness from John Thompson's Wolverhampton works, after a 14-day journey. The load stationary on Forss bridge: The figure in the centre of the picture is Morris Wyatt, Dounreay's site Resident Engineer.

Preparing to lift the vessel into the DFR sphere.

Put to bed: The last anyone will see of the DFR reactor vessel for many years to come.

Like a giant steel Christmas pudding, the DFR sphere stands in the fields of Lower Dounreay. Three times bigger than any similar pressure vessel built in the UK up to that date, the DFR sphere was also the largest in Europe.

By kind permission of Scotsman Publications Ltd.

Day's end: Construction workers leaving the site, March 1957.

Tea-time transport: Buses waiting to take construction workers to their temporary home at the accommodation camp.

Framework for the future: The DFR reactor top showing the internal structure before insertion of the complex array of control and monitoring equipment.

DMTR Heavy Water Plant Room: Removing blanking plates prior to installing the Reactor Aluminium Tank.

DMTR: Lowering the Reactor Aluminium Tank into position.

Assembling one of the DFR Secondary Heat-Exchanger units in which heat from the reactor core was transferred to the water used to raise turbine-driving steam.

Reactor top work well advanced at DMTR. Every square inch of space was utilised in this expertly designed reactor.

Installing the DFR Turbine Alternator, which ran like a sewing machine and generated 15 megawatts of electricity.

Science and agriculture, 1957: Tractor driver James Wares, with George Allan on the binder, harvest Morris Pottinger's corn.

Inserting the DFR Core Skirt: Note the external bearings on which the reactor's Rotating Shield turned.

Visitors 1: Queen Elizabeth the Queen Mother meets the men who built the fast reactor dream . . .

. . . and talks with the young scientists whose task it is to fulfil that dream.

Visitors 2: The Duke of Edinburgh passes a group of workers, some of whom will shortly be on the UKAEA's payroll.

Visitors 3: Mrs Chisholm and son, recently moved into a UKAEA house in Thurso. Mrs Chisholm's husband was then training to be a shift manager at DMTR.

Let there be lights: James Scott's electricians connecting up a street light. Scott's have had a continuous presence at Dounreay since its earliest days.

Reaching completion: DFR Reactor Top with surrounding floor plates lifted.

Learning the ropes: Practising lowering fuel pins into DFR.

Looking south from the roof of DMTR: The pipes in the foreground will connect the reactor's ventilation system with the D1213 stack.

April 1957: Levelling the site for the Royal Navy's Atomic Reactor Training Establishment, ARTE.

The main men: Major-General S.W. Joslin, Works General Manager, and T.G. Williams, the site's Resident Engineer.

The core of the matter: Loading the original DFR core lattice. It was later removed and put on display at the Dounreay Exhibition. The fuelled core, which was only 2 foot in diameter and 2 foot long, generated 60 megawatts of heat.

CHAPTER FOUR

The Approach to Criticality

T he first nuclear chain reaction anywhere in Scotland occurred at Dounreay on Wednesday, August 13th, 1957; not at the fast reactor, nor the Materials Testing Reactor, but at an out-of-the-way corner of the site known as building D1249, the Experimental Criticality Facility, or "Crit". Although this first chain reaction lasted but a moment, its effects have been ongoing for over 40 years.

The Zero Energy Thermal Reactor (ZETR) had been brought to Dounreay from Harwell in 1956. ZETR was a small experimental device designed to investigate what happened when volumes of water containing fissile material came into close proximity with one another. Water, like the human body, is a neutron moderator whose presence in the right quantity, and in the correct geometric configuration, can cause fissile materials to react, starting unplanned, uncontrolled – and undesirable – chain reactions known as criticalities.

Work at the Experimental Criticality Facility had no direct connection with the reactor physics of DFR or DMTR, but it was of vital importance to the design of facilities where nuclear material was present in quantity. Fuel fabrication, fissile material recovery and fuel reprocessing plants were the chief beneficiaries of the work carried out at D1249; and the fact that at no time has there been a criticality incident at Dounreay bears testimony to the success of the Experimental Criticality Group's work all those years ago.

"I'm up here at Dounreay at work in the 'Crit'
In the interests of science I'm doing my bit;
The manager says, I'll go top of the class
If I can achieve the first critical mass."

Anonymous doggerel, written in honour of all those who worked at "The Crit".

A group of would-be scientists pondering possible futures.

Trying to take it all in: Visitors get lessons in nuclear chemistry.

May 11th, 1957: The first site Open Day. A party of visitors en route to the fast reactor.

Labs, lead bricks and remote handling tongs in the D1200 complex, which would soon be the workplace of some of these sightseers.

Exploring new waters: A party of Dounreay fly fishermen at Loch Watten.

Home from home: Ormlie Lodge Hostel.
1. The dining room.

2. An exclusive foot-of-the-stairs social club.

3. The bar complete with waitress service.

Commissioning the core: Charlie Gordon and Jimmy Crossan check DFR instrument tubes.

A DFR Charge Machine and Fuel Transit Flask on the Canning Station: Bill Gunn checks things out. Bill came from Staxigoe and was an early Dounreay recipient of the BEM.

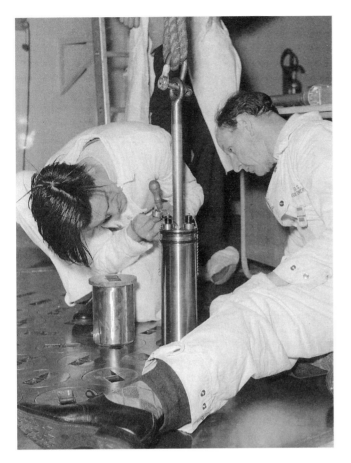

Top left – A right bloody fiddle! Magnus Tait and Bert Gatesman attending to a rig on the DMTR Reactor Top.

Top right – DMTR, preparing to go critical. Exercising a Main Heavy Water Pump Outlet Valve.

Left – Willie Swanson sets up the flow through a rotameter.

Machining DFR fuel elements in the D1201 Fuel Fabrication Plant.

Sam Anthoney finishing off a Mark 1 DMTR fuel element in the D1202 fabrication plant.

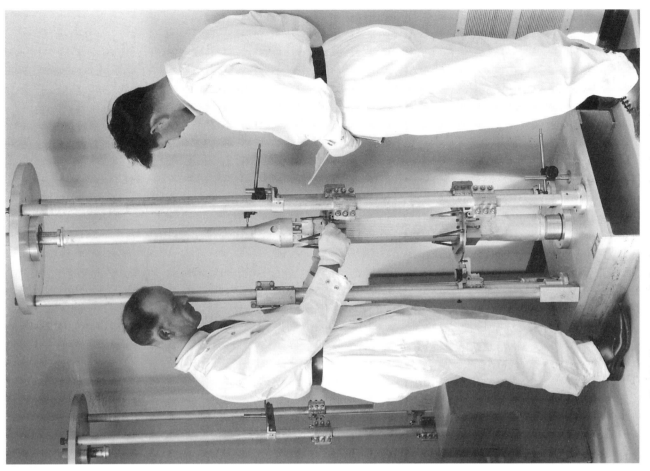

D1202: Dimensional checks on a completed MTR element.

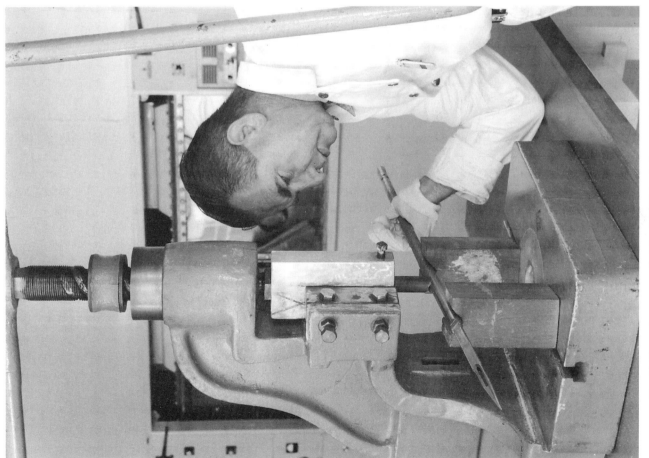

David Gunn inspects a finished DFR fuel element in D1201.

Above – Instrument mechanics overhauling equipment in the main workshop.

Left – Electrician John Hannah tests an "H-H" switch.

Everything safe and secure: The Dounreay Fire Brigade, 1958.

The men of the UKAEA's Dounreay Constabulary.

Charlie Thomson at the Medium Active Panel in the D1204 MTR fuel reprocessing plant: D1204 reprocessed spent fuel from the Harwell reactors before the DMTR started operations.

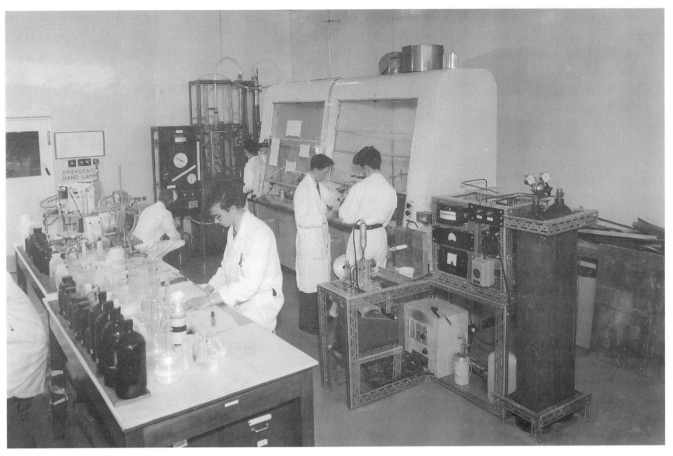

Scientific support: Young chemists carrying out analytical work in one of the D1200 laboratories.

Par for the course: A group of instrument trainees complete their on-site training.

Putting their backs into it: Johnny Duffus yokes up a team of craft apprentices.

Homework at the hostel: Apprentices with a half-built model of a jet plane.

Where history was made: The Control Room at D1249 where, at 1100 hrs on Wednesday, August 13th, 1957, the first ever chain reaction in Scotland was achieved. The standing figure is Ian Paul.

Staff and visitors of the Experimental Criticality Group at D1249: In the background is Cell 1 where the first chain reaction took place. Left to right: Vic Parker, Eric Thornthwaite, Alan Bray, J. C. Smith, Gordon Hansen, Hugh Paxton, John Walford, Roy Reider, Jimmy Lyons, Bob Hack, George White. Hansen, Paxton and Reider were on a visit from the Los Alamos nuclear laboratory in the US.

May 24th, 1958: DMTR goes critical. Bill Picton at the Control Desk with Jimmy Hill, Laurie Holborn and Bill Lunning.

DMTR: The approach to criticality. Loading fresh fuel elements. In the centre of the picture are Charles Tottle, Head of Reactors, and the site Director, Dr Robert Hirst.

The team at play: The first ever dance in the hall at Viewfirth.

Senior staff and their wives at Viewfirth: J.L. Phillips, Reactors Manager; Arthur Parry, Chemical Plant Manager; and Bill Lunning, DMTR.

The younger generation at Viewfirth.

Christmas at Viewfirth. Pints and paper hats: Grown-ups at the bar.

Waiting wide-eyed: In those days no children's Christmas party was complete without a cartoon film show.

Viewfirth, 1958: But this picture sums up a child's Christmas anywhere in the world at any time.

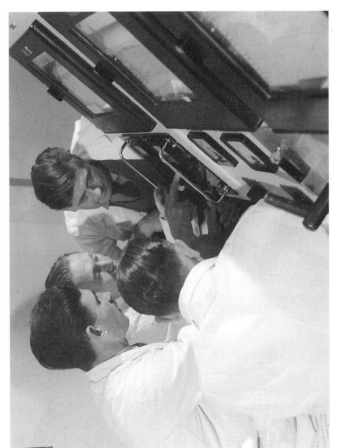

November 14th, 1959: History in the making. The first DFR criticality.

Above left – 10.20hrs: Les Newman notes the first sign that the DFR is about to go critical.

Above right – Cause for satisfaction: Sir William Cook in the DFR Control Room with J.L. Phillips, John Allen, R.R. Matthews and J. Disney of Risley.

Left – 10.52hrs: Shift Manager Peter Haire confirms with Len Wilde and Les Newman that the fast reactor is now a fact.

A job well done: Whatlings plant leaving Dounreay.

CHAPTER FIVE

Fast Reactions – The Working Site

In those days there was a dairy at Thurso East that delivered milk to all over the town and beyond. When the trickle of incomers became a river, spreading out, overflowing the new dwellings on the west side of Thurso, the dairy found itself faced with a problem: it needed a second customer account book. In order to distinguish these come-lately clients from the native Thursonians, the account books were separately labelled: "Locals" and "Atomics". This latter label was carried along with the milk by delivery men who, albeit unwittingly, introduced a new word into the Caithness vocabulary.

"Atomics" brought with them the accents of Lancashire, Clydeside, Aberdeenshire, deepest England, every which place south of the Ord. Some scurried back, others stayed on. Many are still here, their children and grandchildren speaking word-perfect Caithnessian, defying the gloomy predictions of an anonymous UKAEA administrator who, in the early 1960s, advised the Authority to pull out of Dounreay – the place's remoteness made it unattractive to anyone from outwith the Highlands. Outside ideas on "remoteness" were not unknown in Caithness, however.

Born in Wick a century ago, Ian Mackay became a columnist of some repute with the *News Chronicle,* in which paper he told a tale about a visit made to his home town by a Londoner. On being informed by an elderly Wicker that in winter it was not unknown for the Highland Railway's Far North line to block with snow for days on end, the visitor expressed his regrets that such temporary isolation must deny the unfortunate Caithnessians all knowledge of London affairs. "Aye," observed the old Wicker, "that happens now and then. But then the people in London are no better off. They don't know what's going on in Wick, either."

Divine approval: Donald Carmichael shows the Moderator of the Church of Scotland and his Caithness ministers around DFR Control Room.

Everything under control: Shift Manager Geoff Cullington has his finger on the button at the DFR desk.

Foreman Jack Lynch prepares to dispatch a seven-ton flask from DFR.

One of the Charge Machines engaged in routine refuelling operations at DFR.

Bobby Steven concentrates on releasing the flask grab from an irradiated rig being lowered into the storage block in the DMTR active handling bay. Assisting him are Francis Cameron, George Bain and Billy Adamson.

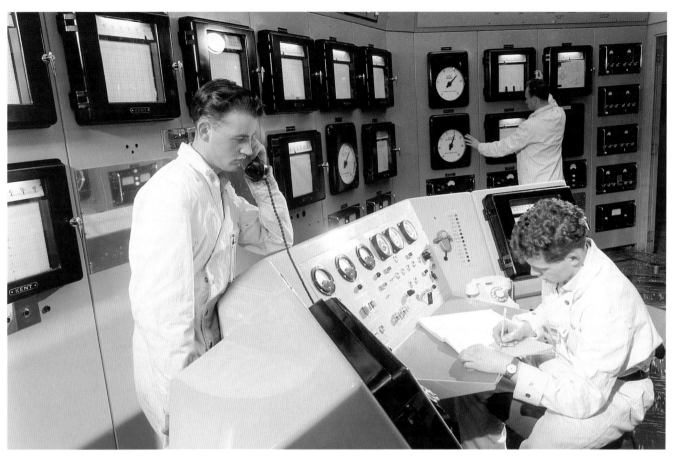

DMTR calling: Bertie Cameron on the Control Room phone. The desk man is James Cormack.

Combined efforts at DMTR: Physicist Doug Henderson, right, watches a member of the Operations team unloading an irradiated specimen from the reactor core. A Health Physics Surveyor keeps a close eye on his monitoring machines.

In the swing of things: A festive season dance at Viewfirth, c.1960.

Something to shout about: Competitors in a Viewfirth Sports Day obstacle race, sometime during the early 1960s.

Houses become homes: St Magnus Road, Thurso, in the early 1960s.

"Atomics" at home in Sigurd Road: James Crossan's wife Jean shows daughters Sandra and Rona the correct way to operate a knitting machine.

Certificate of excellence: The first Dounreay craft apprentice completes his training. Left to right: J. Fleming, M. Wyatt, Hamish Macdonald, A. Spencer, P. McLaren.

Back to the classroom: Dounreay engineers attend a maths lesson at the newly-opened Thurso Technical College.

The man who kept everybody right: Watch repairer David Cargill attends to a time recording clock.

All fired up: The site's Main Boiler House. George Gunn carries out adjustments to Number 2 Boiler.

Early days in D1206, the fast reactor fuel reprocessing plant.
The Inactive Feeds area: Will Ross checks a DCL pump setting, Ronnie Miller stands at the panel.

The Pulse Units which drove active liquor through the mixer-settler boxes where uranium was chemically separated
from fission products. Will Ross adjusts the setting of a weir in one of the mixer-settler boxes. Joe Ross checks the level in
one of the pulse unit "U" tubes.

Left – The D1205 Instrument Shop, 1962. Mechanics at work on a variety of state-of-the-art nucleonic instruments.

Below – The Pond at D1204 MTR Fuel Reprocessing Plant. John Mackenzie operates the dissolver panel while Sandy Ross and Tommy Wright fish for pieces of freshly-cropped fuel element.

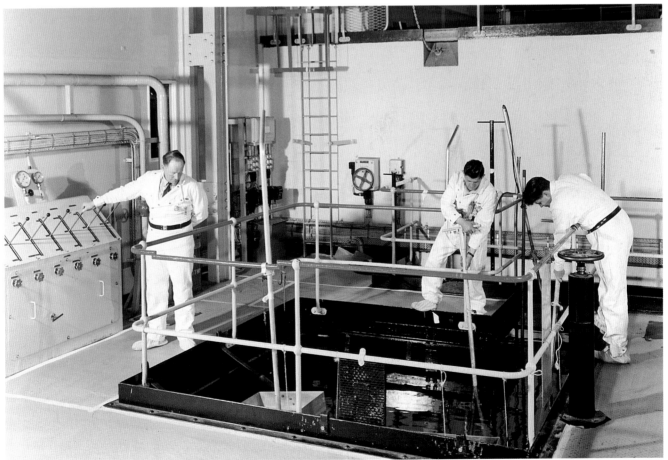

97

"Siberia": The main bay in D1207, the decontamination building, a cold hole at the best of times.

The silent hours squad: DMTR shift workers clocking off. Among this group are Donald Johnston, George Mitchell, Donald Henderson, Sandy Durrand and Willie Swanson.

D1225: The High Active Waste Shaft. A team from DMTR positioning a flask on the waste valve.

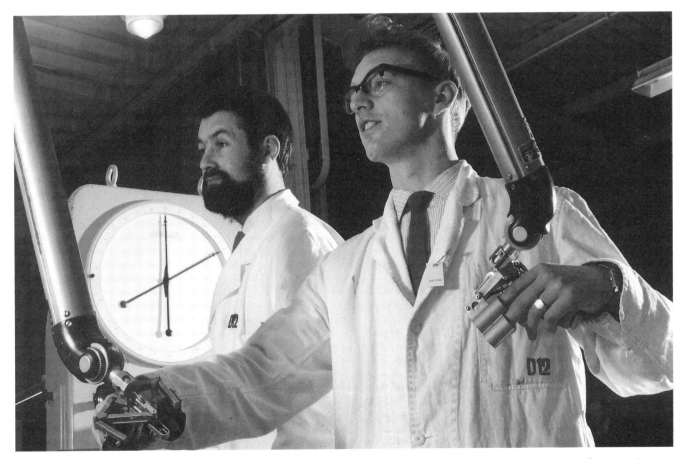

Masters of manipulation: Bob Taylor and Willie Sloss get to grips with things at the D1217 Post-Irradiation Examination cave.

99

Prosperous times: Traill Street, Thurso in the 1960s.

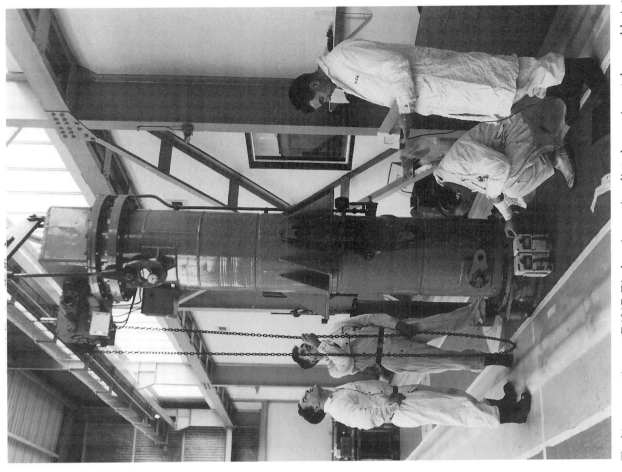

Flasking operations at D1217: Discharging an irradiated experimental assembly into one of the shielded examination caves.

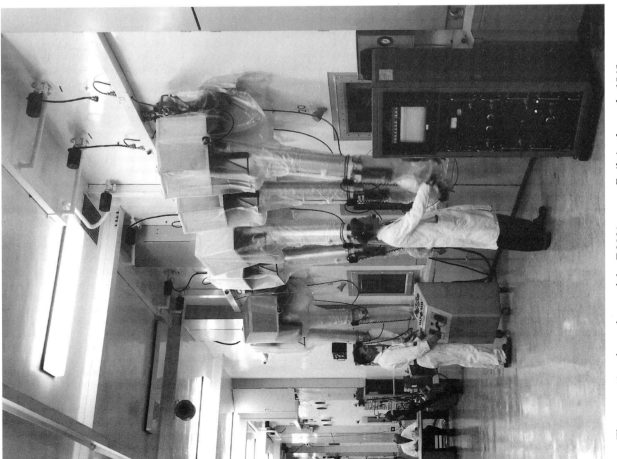

The operating face of one of the D2001 caves: Built in the early 1960s as a post-irradiation examination facility for experimental plutonium fuel elements, D2001 is easily recognised by its unusual wavy roof.

Transport Manager George Scott supervises the loading of a shielded container at Thurso railway station. The container holds an experimental rig for irradiation in DFR. Sale of irradiation space in the reactor earned Dounreay over £5 million.

Houses on the UKAEA's Mount Vernon scheme, 1964.

Thurso Gala 1963: Members of the Dounreay Shinty Club demand money with menaces.

Scientific improvisations in the Fire Brigade Compound. Geoff Leet of Physics Group supervises flow trials on a DMTR Mark 1 fuel element. The dustbin was, apparently, a fully calibrated vessel.

Engineering Development Group: The four-inch experimental loop that replicated one of the DFR Primary NaK circuits.

Engineering Development Group: Willie Polson and Dod Sinclair at the panel for the experimental PFR Sodium Sampling Loop.

Environmental Monitoring 1: Hamish Bremner collects milk at John O'Groats.

Environmental Monitoring 2: Donald Fraser uplifts marine samples from the m.v. *Primula*.

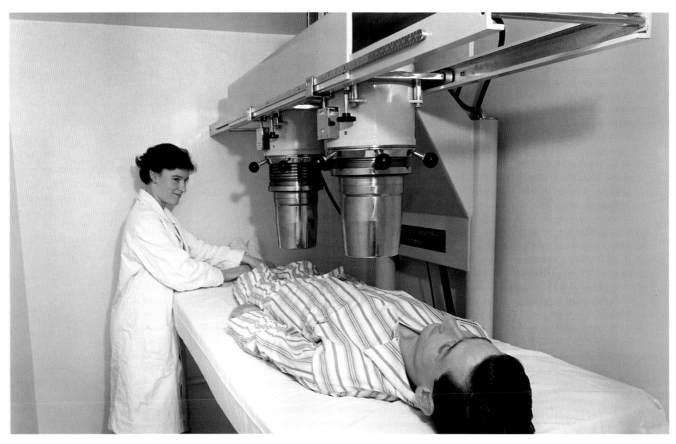

Looking into things: Barbara Mackay operating the Whole Body Monitor which checks for the presence of radioactive particles in the human body.

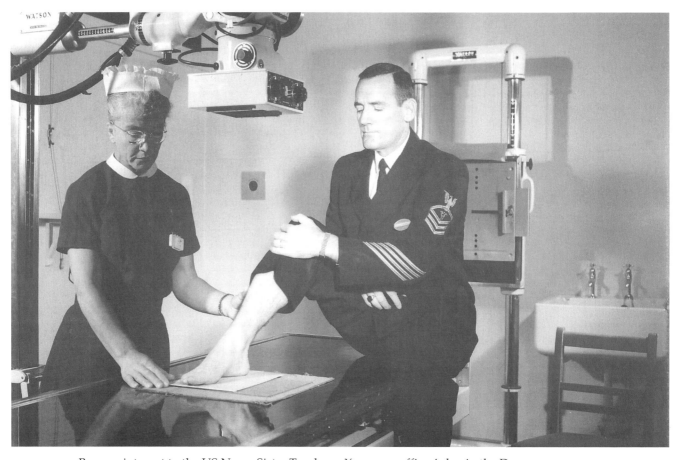

By appointment to the US Navy: Sister Treglown X-rays an officer's leg in the Dounreay surgery.

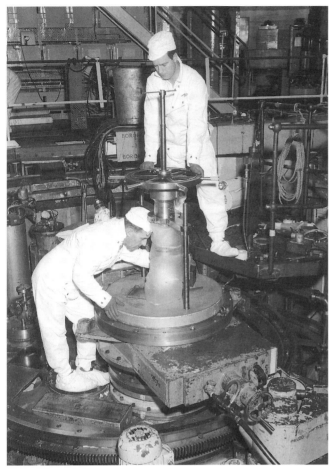

Left – Troubleshooting at DFR, 1965: Dave Spargo and George Sinclair of the Mechanical Engineering Section, recovering a delinquent breeder element.

Below – Serious problems at DFR: In July 1967 a confirmed leak in the primary cooling circuit shut the reactor down for almost a year to enable repairs to be carried out. The leak was in a pipe in the reactor vault, a place to which access was not readily available. The location and repair of this leak remains one of the great achievements of the Dounreay workforce.

Man in a hurry: Willie Dykes carrying the cut-out section of defective pipework.

Operating a facing machine inside the reactor vault, February 1968.

George Watson fitting a facing machine to a section of cooling pipe inside the reactor vault, April 1968.

"Drinka Pinta Milka Day": Sandra Gordon explains the virtues of cow juice to a prospective customer.

Negative developments: John Berriecloth, one of a line of fine photographers collectively responsible for producing almost a quarter of a million pictures of Dounreay and its activities, examines the fruits of his labours.

Main Workshops woodwork section: Among those in the photograph are John Calder, Ray Mackay, Willie Durrand, Donald Waters and Clair Calder.

"Best Workers Dounreay": BWD, those jacks-of-all-trades who did everything from cutting grass to erecting new buildings. Among this group are Hughie Mackay, the first UKAEA industrial employee at Dounreay, Francie Robertson, Peter MacDougall, Donnie Murray, Billy Innes and Hamish MacDonald.

Above – In touch with the outside world: Members of Caithness Amateur Radio Society erecting an aerial.

Left – Local links: Reay Golf Club was always a favourite recreational spot for Dounreay employees.

The days when men were men: Sea bathing was a popular lunchtime diversion at Dounreay before the security fence was built along the foreshore.

Dounreay Exhibition: William Sinclair, the first guide, with a party of boys from Gordonstoun School.

Worldwide interest in Dounreay: Constable Louis Gray directs visiting Nigerian journalists, July 1963.

Naver House, a 70-bed apprentices' hostel, opened its doors in April 1962. Here residents are seen eating breakfast in the dining-room.

Outlines for the future: The Design Office in 1964.

Staff of the UKAEA's Central Superannuation Office. The siting of this office in Thurso was a major boost for the town.

June 22nd, 1968: Site Director Peter Mummery prepares to shut down DMTR for the last time.

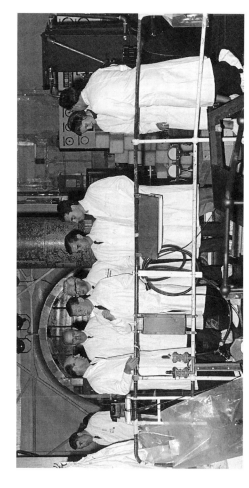

The Secretary of State for Scotland, William Ross, visits DFR with Robert Maclennan, MP for Caithness and Sutherland. Mr Ross claimed the credit for the Government's decision to site the PFR at Dounreay. Shift Manager Mike Tucker (far left) looks unimpressed.

"Air on!" Cooling air being applied to the DMTR Fuel Flask as an element is removed from the reactor during defuelling operations.

CHAPTER SIX

From Caithness to the World – The PFR

Uniquely, perhaps, in the history of modern science, nuclear theory predicted what had not formerly been an observed phenomenon. Prior to 1942 no-one had created a nuclear chain reaction; before 1959 no-one knew with absolute certainty that the DFR would perform in the way its designers assumed it would. But it did, proving that tremendous heat could be generated by a tiny fuel core, that this heat could be transferred, rapidly and efficiently, by liquid metal coolant, and that a worthwhile proportion of this transferred heat could be used to produce turbine-driving steam. DFR operations also revealed that steel swelled in an intense fast neutron flux, a vital discovery for all future fast reactor designs, including its successor, the PFR.

PFR represents a coming of age. It was where boys who signed on as UKAEA craft apprentices a decade or so before graduated into engineers responsible for operating, maintaining, documenting and overseeing the safety of a large nuclear plant. They were not alone; experienced hands from DFR and the Materials Testing Reactor came to join a team which truly did reflect the motto, *From Caithness to the World.*

"The old Fast Reactor was the critical factor
When I was a rising young star.
In the Chemical Group I made nuclear soup,
Then I transferred to DMTR.
At the Sodium Rigs I danced many fine jigs,
Stood my hand in the main Viewfirth Bar.
But the future is clear, to advance my career,
I'll sign up for the new PFR."

Unpublished lines by one "C.D.S.", otherwise anonymous.

June 21, 1966: Sir William Penney cuts the first turf at the site of the Prototype Fast Reactor.

Lifting one of the steel columns for the PFR reactor hall building.

The PFR site in March 1967.

Excavating the PFR decontamination pit.

A welder at work in the PFR reactor vessel.

Positioning the PFR biological shield roof diaphragm plate.

Pipe dreams: A view of the DFR from the site of its successor, the PFR.

April 6th, 1970: The first charter flight from Dounreay takes to the air.

Practical proof of safety: The DFR NaK/water interaction experiment of September 1972, which demonstrated the failure of a jet of hot NaK to ignite on contact with air.

Part of the PFR Alternator Stator casing, en route to Dounreay from Wick Harbour, prepares to negotiate the hairpin bend at the end of Union Street.

A 20-ton section of the PFR reactor jacket passing along Thurso's Princes Street on its way to Dounreay.

One of the three PFR primary sodium pumps being lowered into the reactor vessel.

Locating a dummy sub-assembly in the PFR Core Tank.

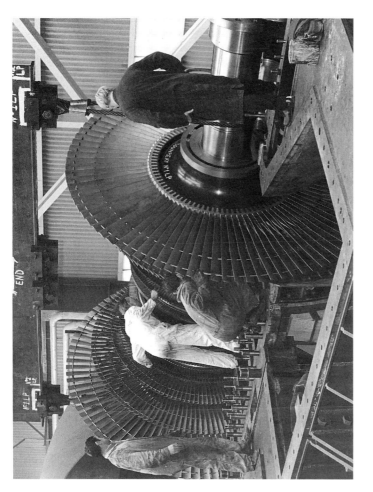

Above – Positioning the PFR low pressure turbine blades.

Left – Piping up one of the three steam drums in the PFR steam-generating building.

February 22nd, 1973: First PFR turbine-alternator electrical synchronisation with the National Grid, using non-nuclear steam. George Bain at the Control Room desk watched by John Walford, Bill Dodd, Gordon Douglas, Derek Shipley and engineers from the generating board.

A month later and the former Royal Navy destroyer boilers used to raise non-nuclear steam for the turbine leave PFR.

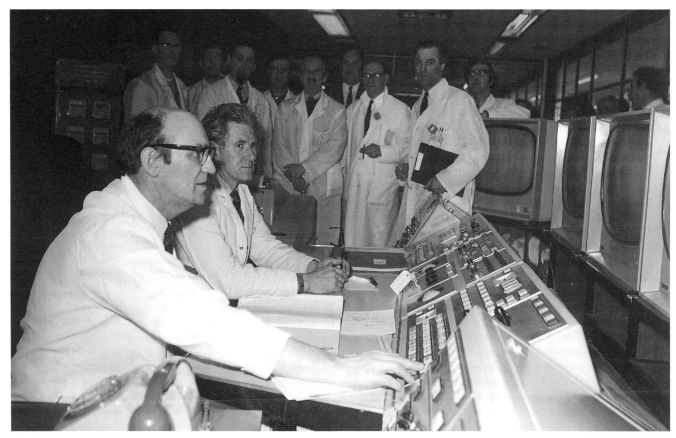

March 3rd, 1974: PFR achieves criticality. Left to right: Ed Adam, Neil Campbell, Charlie Robertson, Don Smith, Ian Walker, Peter Mummery, David Evans, John Walford, Leon Curtis. Peter Miller and Gordon Douglas at the desk.

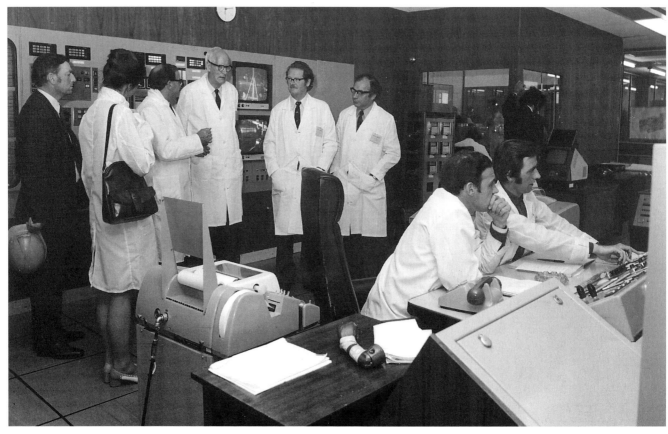

Twenty years down the line from the DFR: August 14th, 1974. Christopher Hinton, now Lord Hinton of Bankside, visits PFR Control Room. To his left is Station Manager David Evans, while Bill Smith and George Bain man the control desk.

D1206 Fast Reactor fuel reprocessing plant refurbishment.

2. Installing new pipework at the Inactive Feeds section of the plant.

1. Sitting in the middle of it all: Removing the conveyor tunnel floor.

3. A pair of workers inside the Active Filter Change Facility which was designed to allow the safe replacement of active ventilation filters.

Space for future expansion: A new tank being lowered into the D1208 High Active Liquor Storage facility.

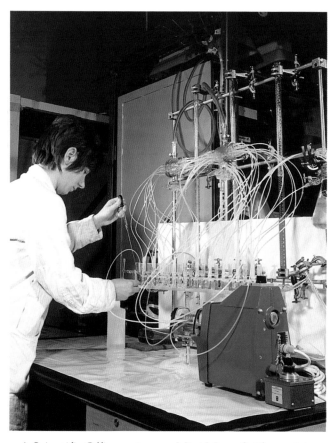

A Scientific Officer sets up a Mini Mixer Settler unit in Lab 80 of the D1200 complex.

March 28th, 1977: DFR closes down. Thurso civic dignitaries, including John Sinclair and Isabella Cormack, in the sphere.

DFR closure: Clifford Blumfield and Fred Barclay present a model of the reactor to its great champion, Lord Hinton of Bankside.

131

The original PFR simulator, a training facility used by reactor operators from all over the world.

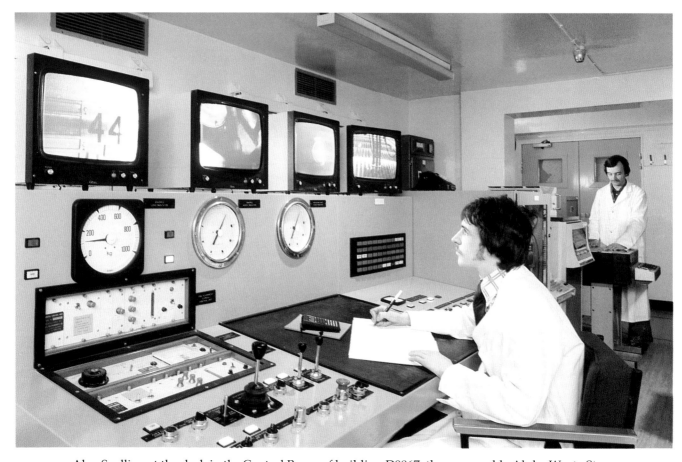

Alan Scullion at the desk in the Control Room of building D9867, the recoverable Alpha Waste Store.

PFR refuelling operations in progress, April 1979.

Twenty years is a long time in the field of information technology. This Data 100 computer was top-of-the-range in 1978.

Jeanette Shearer demonstrates the art of Highland dancing to a group of delegates to a 1969 Fast Reactor Conference at Dounreay, seen here relaxing at the Portland Arms, Lybster.

Iain Sutherland, chairman of the Wick Society, local historian, well-known authority on the herring fishing industry and a UKAEA employee for 28 years, settling accounts at the Dounreay canteen.

True to type: 1978 secretarial trainees acquiring keyboard skills.

135

Preaching the nuclear gospel: A Dounreay exhibition at Thurso Technical College.

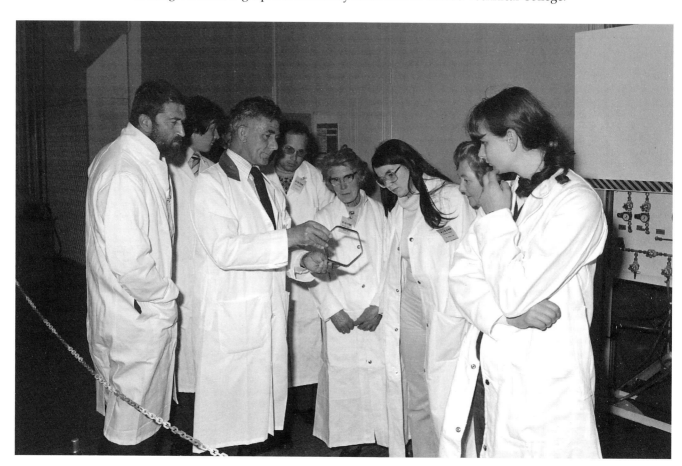

Open Day 1979: PFR plant engineer Dave Sprague gives a practical demonstration.

An aerial view of the Dounreay site as it was in the late 1970s.

Altnabreac Station, April 1979: Robin, Lord Thurso, inspects core-samples from the drillings carried out by geologists on land nearby as part of the search for a suitable site for a national radioactive waste repository.

CHAPTER SEVEN

Days of Change and Challenge

Coincident with the start of PFR fuel reprocessing, out in the wider world a new political philosophy set to work. While all around it the working landscape shuddered under the impact of policies designed to make British industry "leaner and fitter", Dounreay continued its steady progress towards the goal of a commercial fast reactor. Safe within a bubble of secure employment, the Dounreay workforce developed its expertise and refined its specialist skills, unaffected by the radical shake-outs which threw millions of people onto the unemployment midden. There was, perhaps, a feeling that the modernisation of the old metal bashing-based industries was a thing long overdue, that the dust, dirt and grime associated with coal-fired energy supplies did not fit in with the clean-cut computerised society that was rapidly taking shape throughout the 1980s. After all, as the sticker proclaimed – *Fast Reactors for the Future.*

"The Government has carried out a review of this programme in the light of the expectation that commercial deployment of fast reactors in the UK will not now be required for 30 to 40 years. . . We have therefore decided to fund the reactor until the end of the financial year 1993/94."

July 21st, 1988: The Secretary of State for Energy, Cecil Parkinson, informs the House of Commons of the Government's intention to end public-funded research into fast breeder reactors.

Above – DFR decommissioning starts: Alex Gillies, dressed in full protective clothing, dismantles a cold trap, once used for removing impurities from liquid metal coolant.

Left – DFR decommissioning: Monty Frost carrying out a gas check around the Reactor Transfer Valve.

PFR – "Preparing for Reprocessing": Commissioning engineer Tom Dodd checks the pin cropping machine in the D1206 Fuel Breakdown Cave.

The cutting edge: A laser slices through the outer wrapper of a PFR spent fuel sub-assembly in the D1206 Breakdown Cave.

Chris Cormack and Alex Potts lining up the PFR spent fuel flask at the Posting-in Port to the D1206 Fuel Breakdown Cave.

Jim Mackay at the desk in the new Control Room, D1206.

Operating the Pond Transporter in the PFR Buffer Store, where irradiated fuel sub-assemblies are stored underwater prior to dispatch to D1206 for reprocessing.

State-of-the-arts: Dounreay has always been at the forefront of technologies relevant to its nuclear activities. Scientific Officers are here seen setting up a Thermal Ionisation Mass Spectrometer in Lab 75 of the D1200 complex.

Checking alignments using laser holography in building D8542.

A hand on the levers of power: Winnie Ewing, Member of the European Parliament for the Highlands and Islands, at the controls of the remote drum handling machine in D9867, the Recoverable Alpha Waste Store.

Knowledge for the taking: Ruth James issues a book from the Dounreay Library.

September 1983: Thurso Townswomen's Guild on a visit to the Dounreay Exhibition.

Above – The 40-foot operating floor of the PFR Steam Generating Building showing the water side pipework to the steam-raising vessels. Alan Munro and Evan Park consult a drawing.

Left – Engineer Sue Matthews alongside the PFR turbine.

Money with menaces: Brian Durrans is taken hostage in the interests of the 1985 Children in Need Appeal, for which the Dounreay trainees raised £1500.

No champagne at this christening! Deputy Site Director Jack Smedley names a Class 37 diesel locomotive "Dounreay" at Thurso Station in June 1985.

Life beyond the gates: Dounreay employees with outside interests. John Macrae, piper; musicians Christine Brown and Derek Mosedale; coastguard Geoff Leet; Douglas MacRoberts, minister; crofter Peter Bates; John Porter, radio interviewer; Hugh MacLeod, creel fisherman; and trout angler Keith Lorimer.

Kathryn Cartwright displays a model of the proposed European Demonstration Reprocessing Plant at an exhibition in the former Co-op store in Thurso. The EDRP Inquiry which took place in Thurso Town Hall lasted 95 days and resulted in the UKAEA and BNFL being given approval to build the EDRP. Changes in future fast reactor policy by European governments have rendered this decision academic.

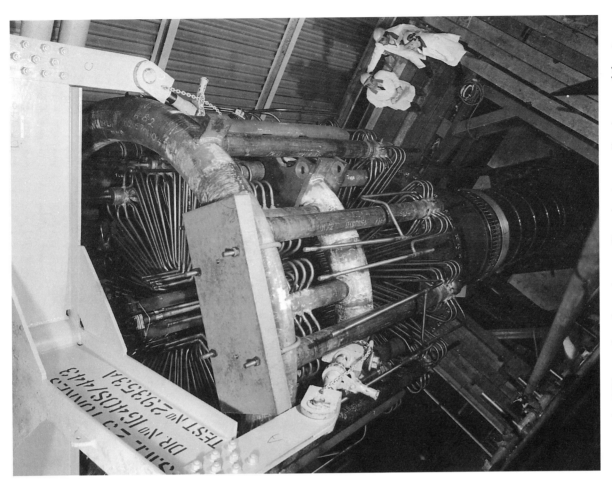

In 1986 the PFR was shut down by a sodium/water reaction in one of the steam-generating vessels on the non-nuclear side of the plant. This led to a programme of upgrading with the vessel internals being replaced by improved units. Here a new reheater is being lifted from its storage frame.

Routine operations in the PFR Reactor Hall: Lowering the Charge Hole Instrument Plug into its storage position.

The invisible made visible: The effects of gamma radiation moderated by water are clearly seen in this shot of spent fuel elements stored in the DMTR pond.

Above – June 1987: The final section of the barrier being lowered into position.

Left – For the first 10 years of PFR's life the ingress of large quantities of seaweed into the cooling water pumphouse dogged the plant's operations. In 1986 Taylor Woodrow were contracted to build a seaweed barrier. Early work in progress on one of the barrier's piles.

Opened in May 1986 by former UKAEA Chairman Lord Marshall, the D2670 Fuel Cycle Development Laboratory was intended as a proving ground for the new techniques that EDRP would bring to reprocessing. Here Peter Thompson is seen checking a level in one of the pulsed columns.

Above – Setting a stamp on things: Staff marking up items in the D8525 bonded store.

Left – The segregation and safe storage of radioactive waste has always been an important part of Dounreay operations. Here, drums containing low active waste are being stacked in one of the site's waste pits.

July 9th, 1987: The Secretary of State for Energy, Cecil Parkinson, in the PFR Control Room with UKAEA Chairman John Collier and senior PFR staff Ed Adam and Peter Gallie. Desk Operator Walter Smith keeps the power steady at 250 megawatts.

Earlier that day, Cecil Parkinson visited the D1206 fast reactor fuel reprocessing plant where Owen Pugh, head of the Fuel Cycle Area, explained the plant's function. At the left of the picture, Dounreay Director Gerry Jordan looks thoughtful.

Old ways, new technology: Dounreay Health Physics staff wait to collect a sample for analysis as Mrs Bradford milks her goat at Blackhills, Reay.

"This is how it's done nowadays, mum": Trainee Parents' Day, 1987.

Another new building at Dounreay in the 1980s was D2900, a modern decontamination facility. Plant operators watch a "Carousel" flask being lowered into a soak tank.

Built as part of a long-term strategy for the safe disposal of radioactive waste, the Dounreay Cementation Plant started commissioning trials in 1988. Archie MacMillan prepares to post a waste drum into the packaging facility.

In 1986, as a first step to eventual part-privatisation, the UKAEA became a trading fund. An early Commercial Opportunities Paper described an electro-chemical method of disposing of toxic wastes. This resulted in the construction of the Silver II Rig, seen here with Dr David Steele and fellow scientist Kathryn Cartwright.

CHAPTER EIGHT

The Nineties and Beyond

Let no-one be under any illusion: had Dounreay been a conventional industrial complex, the gates would have closed long ago. But fast reactors breed slow consequences.

As early as 1947 it was recognised that the chief barriers in the path towards large-scale nuclear power development were the economics involved in making the technology competitive with other forms of energy production, and the safe permanent disposal of radioactive waste. The first barrier was used to justify the mothballing of the UK fast reactor programme; the second has guaranteed that Dounreay will continue to be a major source of employment in Caithness for several decades yet.

Nuclear time is akin to the multi-million year scale of geological time, a scale beside which the total span of human existence appears so relatively short. No-one alive today knows whether or not there will be human beings on this earth 150,000 years from now. But assuredly, legacies of the decommissioned Dounreay Fast Reactor projects will still be present in one form or another, encapsulated in glass, stored in cement-filled containers, or packed into steel drums. The preparation, storage and ultimate safe disposal of these legacies are primary tasks that will occupy the Dounreay workforce for many years to come.

And in the end? Well, who knows? A greenfield site, perhaps, or a collection of crumbling old buildings beside the surging Atlantic, which may inspire some poetic soul to write as a kindred spirit did almost a century ago:

"Brother, say what is this lonely tower?
'Tis the Castle of Downreay, ruined and hoar,
And it gleams through a smirr of the cold night shower
In the beauty of old romantic lore;
The nettle grows rank in the chinks of its door;
The machar keeps well hidden gold-pot and crock;
The chief and his henchmen have long paid their score,
But the waves still foam to the castle rock."

From "Downreay Castle", by John W. Macleod. 1875-1919.

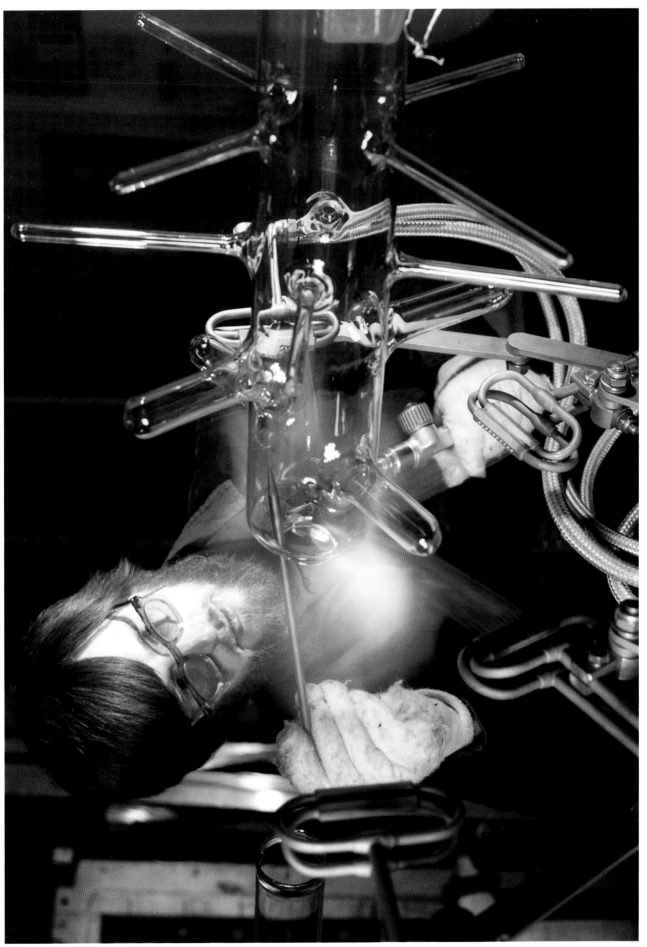

Science as art: Dounreay glass-blower Ian Pearson at work.

June 28th, 1990: Leslie Rowe and George Malcolm say *"bon voyage"* to the crew of the final Dounreay charter flight.

Jump to it! Constable Andrew Farquhar puts "Jasper" through his paces.

Open for business: The staff of AEA Technology's Fuel Services Division outside their newly-built HQ, D6000, with UKAEA Chairman Dr Brian Eyre.

Fuel Services in action: Preparing to post an irradiated component into the D1206 Fuel Breakdown Cave.

161

Fuel services for the future: Steve Beckett and Brian Spence checking out new equipment in the D1206 Residue Recovery Plant.

Above – Committed to renewable energy research: AEA technicians installing an anemometer at Hill of Forss as part of a projected wind-farm scheme.

Left – Committed to responsible waste disposal: Night work in progress at one of the test bores carried out at Dounreay on behalf of NIREX, the nuclear industry's radioactive waste executive.

Midsummer 1992: A small-hours shot of the Penrod 64 Rig that assisted with the installation of the new low active liquid effluent pipeline.

Above – Dounreay workers on the march: Director Gerry Jordan outside the main Administration building with some of the employees who took part in the march through Inverness in January 1991 to draw attention to the social consequences of the decision to close the PFR.

Left – Diversification was a keynote of the early 1990s. The staff of the Tubular Descaling Plant which removes radioactive scale from inside pipes used in the offshore oil industry.

Another '90s innovation at Dounreay was the supercompactor designed to reduce the volume of low active waste.

Keeping an eye on the plant: Alan Elder and George Macleod recording tank levels in the D1204 MTR fuel reprocessing plant.

Hands up for good causes. Above: Dounreay Director Gerry Jordan presents a cheque to Thurso Brownies and Guides. Below: Members of Thurso Swimming Club jump for joy at a donation of £500 from the UKAEA.

Getting in about it: Stephen Sutherland of JGC Welding working inside a vessel at D1249, the Sodium/Water Reaction test facility.

Another major engineering challenge at PFR was the need to carry out repairs to the steam-generating vessels. Here, engineers Alan Peters and Harry Bridge pose with staff from Nicolson Engineering and UKAEA operations personnel in front of the "Cocoa Tin", which contains a well-shrouded evaporator unit.

A world first for Dounreay was the removal and replacement of the three primary sodium pump filters from the PFR. Here a filter is being lowered from the 36-inch flask into the shielded filter replacement facility.

Over 500 years of accumulated experience is represented in this picture of the Fuel Technology Group on the eve of its disbandment in March 1993.

A matter of life or death: Willie Sutherland shows his fellow Dounreay firemen an oystercatcher chick, freshly rescued from a drainpipe.

No reprieve: March 31st, 1994. Shift Manager Gordon Blagden starts to reduce power at PFR, watched by the former UKAEA Chairman, Sir John Hill, David Manson, Dr Brian Eyre and Ed Adam.

Midnight on 31st March, 1994: Members of the shift team who put the plant to bed for the last time gather in the PFR Control Room.

June 27th, 1995: Another PFR milestone. Robbie Henderson and the "Grouse Beaters" on the reactor top after removing the final fuel sub-assembly from the core, thus completing phase one of the PFR decommissioning project ahead of schedule.

Sign on the dotted line: Senior staff from AEAT, UKAEA, W.S. Atkins and NNC sign the contract to dispose of 1500 tons of PFR sodium.

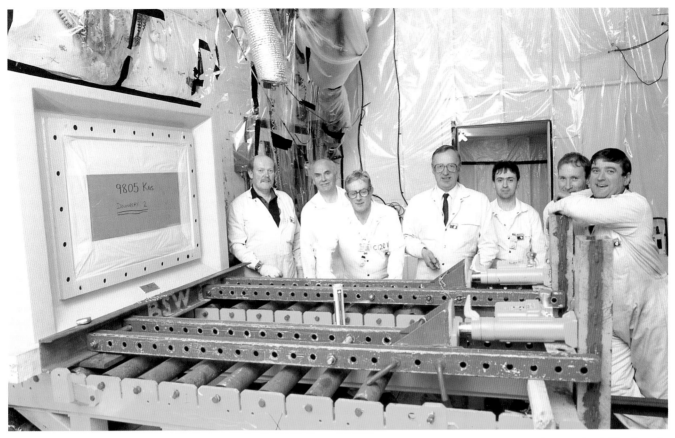

All smiles at a job well done: Engineering Support Group and Operations staff celebrate the completion of a difficult task – the replacement of one of the zinc bromide-filled windows in the D1206 Breakdown Cave.

Futures for the past: Decommissioning work in progress at DFR in the 1990s.

Out with the old: Demolition under way in the PFR Turbine Hall, November 1995.

And in with the new: R.J. McLeod start work on the Sodium Disposal Plant in the former PFR Turbine Hall.

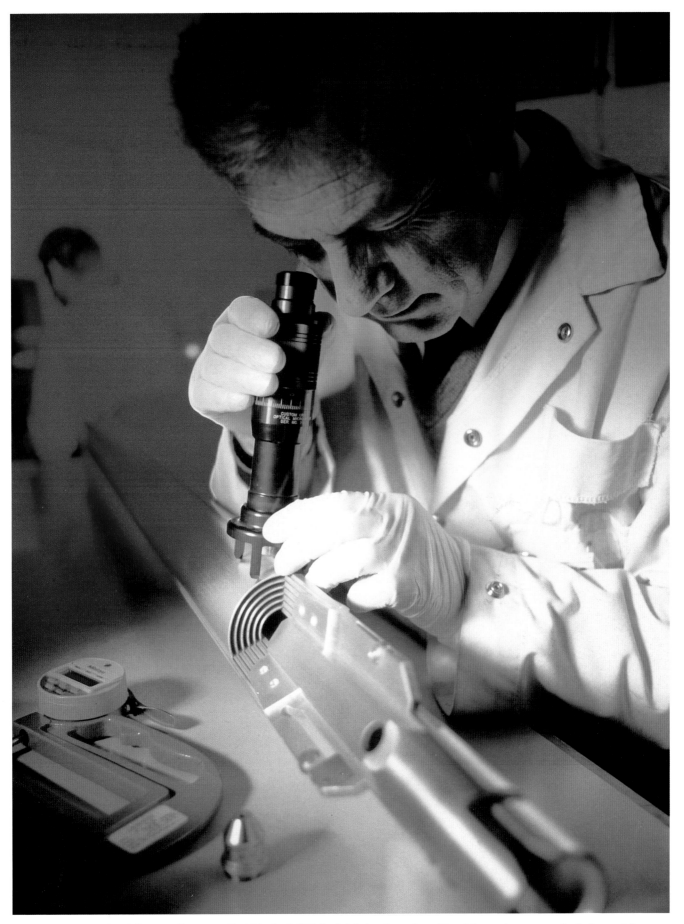

Continuing demand for excellence: In D1202, the MTR fuel fabrication plant, Roy Munro inspects a fuel element for an export order.

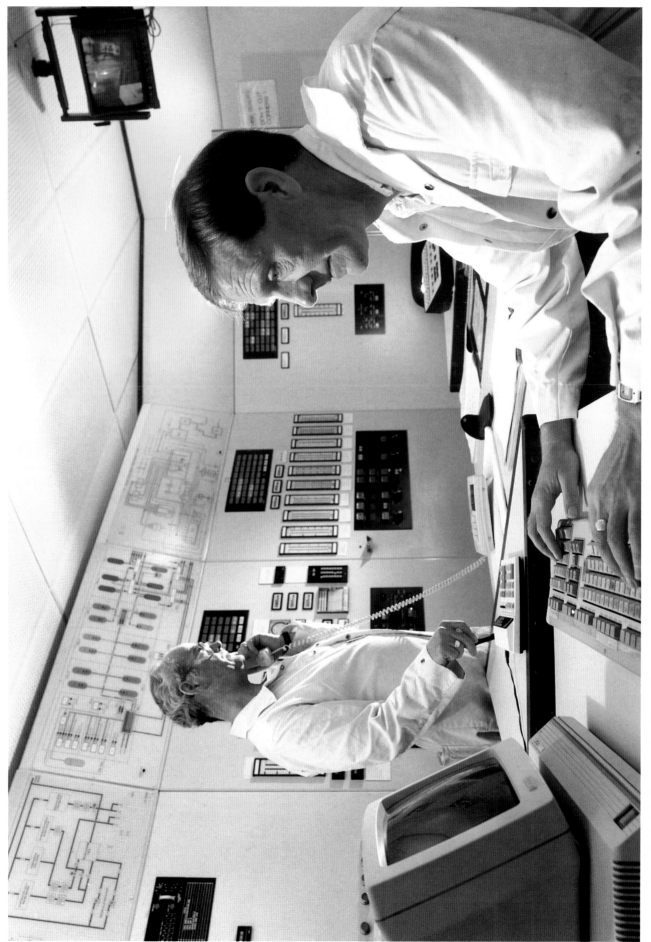

The plant at their fingertips: Davie Dunnett and Iain Davidson in the Control Room of the D1208 High Active Liquor Storage and Treatment Plant.

Gallons of good fun: Halkirk Playgroup in training with the Dounreay Fire Brigade, May 1995.

Helping the Caithness community: Sarah Coghill and Isobel Powell present Halkirk Rainbow Guides with new uniforms funded by the UKAEA.

Birmingham-bound Dounreay secretaries prepare to board a charter flight at Wick Airport, en route to a 1997 training course.

On the ball: Dounreay staff line up for a game of football at the new Naver Field sports facility, May 1997.

Safety first 1: A plant operator changes a bottle of Anhydrous Hexafluoride gas in D1203, the Uranium Recovery Plant.

Safety first 2: Alex Potts makes out a Permit to Work Certificate, without which no work can be undertaken at Dounreay.

Above – Halkirk folk at the Dounreay Open Day, June 1998. Kirsty Robertson with grandfather Charlie Miller and Shona Campbell.

Left – Full circle: Almost 60 years after her photograph was taken on the steps of the Lower Dounreay farmhouse, Elizabeth Nicolson, née Davidson, poses there with her own daughter, Monica, in May 1998.